Teacher Resource

COMPREHENSION ACTIVITIES

Key Stage 1/P1-P3

Book 1

BRIGHTER ®
VISION

Brighter Vision Education Ltd.,
Eton House, 18-24 Paradise Road, Richmond, Surrey TW9 1SR

Copyright 1999 Brighter Vision Education Ltd.

® is a registered trademark of the publisher.

Some material used in this edition is used under licence from
Frank Schaffer Publications Inc.

Consultant Editor: Pam Hutchinson

BV-05-307 Teacher Resource Comprehension Activities Key Stage 1/P1-P3 Book 1
ISBN 1 86172 157 9

Introduction

This set of 88 graded reading and follow-up activities has been designed to support the teaching of a wide range of reading skills and to help your pupils to understand and appreciate what they read. The activities are particularly appropriate for 5-7 year-olds.

Since the children in this age group develop their reading skills at different rates the collection provides valuable practice and reinforcement material for all levels of experience.

The content list gives information about the skills covered in each activity and this information is repeated on the separate photocopiable sheets. The skills covered include:

★   classification
★   sequencing
★   noting details
★   following instructions
★   determining cause and effect
★   recognising similarities and differences
★   character analysis
★   predicting outcomes
★   literal comprehension
★   drawing inferences

The activities provide a wide variety of content and design to stimulate the children and to encourage them to read with care, interest and above all, enjoyment. Select from this rich resource for valuable comprehension work both in the classroom and for homework.

Contents

Contents

Rainbowsaurus

Name _____

Colour the spots with **toy** words **yellow**.
Colour the spots with **clothing** words **red**.
Colour the spots with **animal** words **blue**.

kite

doll

fish

hen

dress

coat

ball

hat

bike

dog

cat

shoe

pig

Comprehension, KS1

Group It

Name _____

Fill in the circles next to words that belong in each group.

1. Colours
- ○ red
- ○ blue
- ○ truck
- ○ green
- ○ cat
- ○ yellow

2. Food
- ○ bat
- ○ milk
- ○ egg
- ○ meat
- ○ dress
- ○ apple

3. People
- ○ tree
- ○ girl
- ○ mother
- ○ father
- ○ boy
- ○ fox

4. Numbers
- ○ five
- ○ one
- ○ frog
- ○ three
- ○ four
- ○ sock

5. Parts of the Body
- ○ ear
- ○ arm
- ○ hand
- ○ head
- ○ nose
- ○ shoe

6. Weather
- ○ grass
- ○ rain
- ○ cloud
- ○ fog
- ○ boot
- ○ snow

7. School
- ○ book
- ○ desk
- ○ sun
- ○ pencil
- ○ flag
- ○ bird

8. House
- ○ lamp
- ○ bed
- ○ door
- ○ sink
- ○ hat
- ○ rug

Try This! Make a list of baby animal names.

Comprehension, KS1

Name That Tiger

Skill: Classification

Name _____

Write the word from the Word Box that tells about the list of words on each tiger.

Word Box
space   farm
tools   insects
food   dishes

barn
horse
cow

1. _____

bowl
plate
cup

2. _____

drill
hammer
saw

3. _____

sun
moon
stars

4. _____

bee
ladybird
butterfly

5. _____

apple
milk
cheese

6. _____

Try This!   Add one more word to the list on each tiger

Comprehension, KS1

Name _____

Write names of things that belong in each group.

Things at the Beach

_____

_____

_____

Kinds of Clothes

_____

_____

_____

Animals That Swim

_____

_____

_____

Parts of a Tree

_____

_____

_____

Things in a Salad

_____

_____

_____

Try This! Draw pictures of the things in one of the lists above

Comprehension, KS1

Skill: Classification

Name _____

Use the words in the Word Box.
Write another word for each group.

Word Box

jump	stars
four	plum
toes	shoes
month	blue
dinner	butter

1. apple, pear, _____

2. hop, skip, _____

3. two, three, _____

4. shirt, pants, _____

5. red, white, _____

6. legs, feet, _____

7. day, week, _____

8. breakfast, lunch, _____

9. peanut butter, bread, _____

10. sun, moon, _____

Try This! Write a word that tells about each group of words above. Example: apple, pear, plum - fruit

Comprehension, KS1

Name _____

Circle names of things in the picture.

mother	soil	gloves
apple	boy	blocks
pots	flowers	plants
grass	cat	cake

Circle and write the best title for the picture.

Picking Flowers   Planting Time   My School

_____

Try This! Say why the other two titles are not as good.

Comprehension, KS1

Rabbit and Mouse

Name _____

Look at the picture.
Circle and write the best title.

Rabbit has a rest
Sleeping Rabbit

Rabbit Friends
The Rabbit Nest

Snow in Winter
Time to Play

Brown Mouse
Asleep for the Winter

Try This! Write a story about one of the pictures above.

Comprehension, KS1

Skill: Main idea.
Choosing a title

Name _____

Cut out the titles.
Match and paste them to each picture.

1. [ ]

2. [ ]

3. [ ]

4. [ ]

I Can Draw	Run and Kick
The New Dad	On Her Toes

Comprehension, KS1

Cat and Dog

Name _____

Colour and cut out the small pictures.
Paste them on the big picture.
Write a title for your picture.

_____

Comprehension, KS1

The Dog

Name _____

List things you see in the picture.

_____   _____

_____   _____

_____   _____

Write a title for the picture.

_____

 Try This! Write a story about the picture

Comprehension, KS1

Animals

Name _____

| The **main idea** tells about the whole picture. |

Does the sentence tell the main idea of the picture?
Fill in **yes** or **no**. Then write the main idea sentence.

	Yes	No
1. The dog plays.	○	○
2. The dogs are big and little.	○	○

	Yes	No
1. The chick is hatching.	○	○
2. The chick is big.	○	○

	Yes	No
1. The pet is furry.	○	○
2. She loves her pet.	○	○
3. Her pet is little.	○	○

 **Try This!** Draw pictures of four animals you like.

11

Comprehension, KS1

At the Circus

Name _____

> The **main idea** tells about the whole picture.

Cut out the main idea sentences.
Match and paste them to the pictures.

1. [ ]

2. [ ]

3. [ ]

4. [ ]

| She rides on the horse. | He did a magic trick. |
| The dogs are silly. | The funny clown juggles. |

Comprehension, KS1

Name _____

The **main idea** tells about the whole picture.

Which sentence tells the main idea of the picture?
Fill in the circle next to the correct answer.

1.

- ○ The cat has a tail.
- ○ The cat hunts mice.

2.

- ○ The bat has wings.
- ○ The bat can hang upside down.

3.

- ○ The tree frog is green.
- ○ The tree frog can climb.

4.

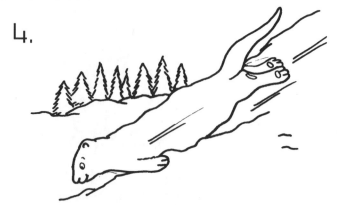

- ○ The river otter is playing.
- ○ It is snowing.
- ○ The river otter has fur.

5.

- ○ The boy is happy.
- ○ The giraffe is taller than the boy.
- ○ Giraffes have long necks.

Cut out a picture from an old magazine. Paste it on
writing paper. Write a sentence that tells the main idea.

Comprehension, KS1

Name _____

| The **main idea** tells about the whole picture. |

Which sentence tells the main idea of the picture?
Fill in the circle next to the correct answer.

1.

○ The flowers are pretty.
○ The boy smells the flowers.

2.

○ The bird feeds her babies.
○ The babies are in the nest.

3.

○ The leaves are falling.
○ It is a windy day.

4.

○ The butterfly is on the tree.
○ The girl sees the butterfly.
○ It is spring.

5.

○ The girl is outside.
○ The plants are growing.
○ The girl waters the flowers.

Find a picture in a book. Copy it on drawing paper.
Write a sentence that tells the main idea.

Comprehension, KS1

The Sea

Name _____

> The **main idea** tells about the whole picture.

Cut out the small pictures. Paste them on the big pictures any way you like to show something happening. Write a sentence that tells the main idea of each picture.

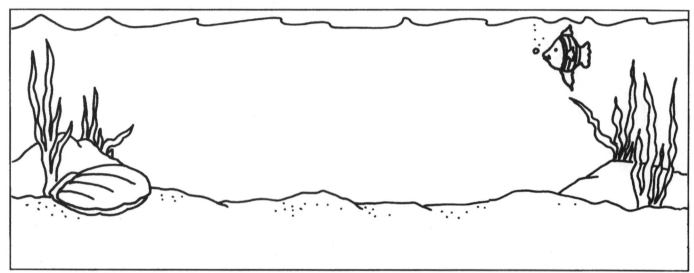

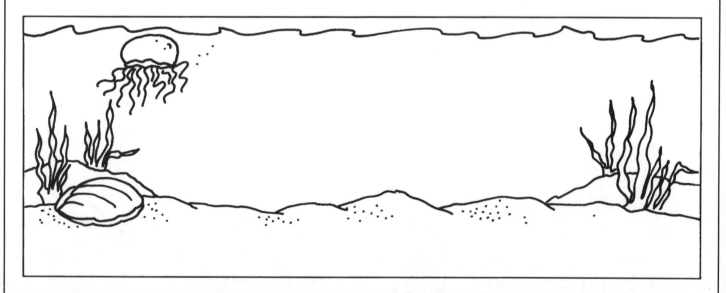

Comprehension, KS1

Camping

Name _____

| The **main idea** tells about the whole story. |

Read the story.

Mike helped pitch the tent.
Amy cooked a hot dog.
Dad told a funny story.
They liked camping.

Does the sentence tell the main idea? Write **yes** or **no**.

1. Amy cooked a hot dog. _____

2. Dad told a funny story. _____

3. They liked camping. _____

4. Mike helped pitch the tent. _____

Write the sentence that tells the main idea.

_____

List things you need to take on a camping trip.

Comprehension, KS1

Dinner Time

Name _____

| The **main idea** tells about the whole story. |

Read the story.

We went out for dinner.
Ben had a hamburger.
Dad had a salad.
I had spaghetti.
Mum had pancakes.

Does the sentence tell the main idea?
Write **yes** or **no**.

1. I had spaghetti. _____

2. Ben had a hamburger. _____

3. Dad had a salad. _____

4. We went out for dinner. _____

5. Mum had pancakes. _____

Write the sentence that tells the main idea.

_____

Write a story for this main idea: It was a bad storm.

Comprehension, KS1

Nancy and Mario

Skill: Main idea of a story

Name _____

The **main idea** tells about the whole story.

Cut, match, and paste the pictures.
Circle the sentence in each story that tells the main idea.

Nancy went on a hiking trip.

She had a special helper.

It was a llama.

The llama carried her pack.

Mario was very excited.

He tried on a space suit.

He ate space food.

He sat in a rocket seat.

Space camp was great!

Comprehension, KS1

Jean, Jim and Joe

Name _____

The **main idea** tells about the whole story.

Read each story.
Circle the sentence below it that tells the main idea.

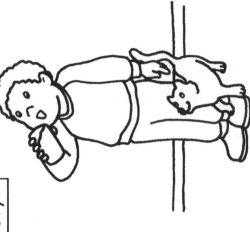

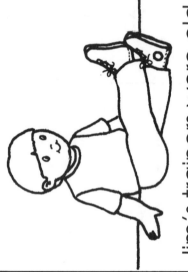

Jean lost her teddy bear.
She looked in the
cupboard. She checked
the shelf. Then she found
the bear in her toy box.
She gave it a big hug.

Jean hugged the bear.
Jean had a toy box.
Jean found her lost bear.

Jim's trainers were old.
They had holes in them.
His mum took him to the
shoe shop. He got a new
pair of shoes. They had
red and blue shoelaces.

Mum went shopping.
The shoes had holes.
Jim got new shoes.

Joe was drinking milk.
Suddenly he felt
something furry rub
against his leg. It was his
cat. She wanted some
milk, too. Joe put some in
her dish.

Joe was scared.
The cat wanted milk, too.
Joe's cat was furry.

Write a four-sentence story. Let a friend find the main idea of the story.

The Turtle and the Fox

Name _____

| The **main idea** tells about the whole story. |

Read the story carefully. Look at all the details in the story.
Then write a sentence telling the main idea.

Shelby lives in the woods.
She is a little turtle.
Shelby can do tricks.
This is her best one.
She turns over and spins
on her shell.

Red Fox likes to drive his car.
One day he drove too fast.
A police officer stopped him.
She gave Red Fox a ticket.
That was not fun.
Now Red Fox drives slowly.

Write a title for each story.

Comprehension, KS1

Jack's Beetle

Name _____

Jack ran in the park.
He ran after a beetle.
The little beetle hid in the grass.
Jack looked and looked.
But he did not find it.

1. Where did Jack run?

    _____

2. What did Jack do?

    _____

3. Was the beetle big or little?

    _____

4. Where did the beetle hide?

    _____

5. Who looked and looked?

    _____

6. Did Jack find the beetle?

    _____

The Lost Kitten

Name _____

A little, grey kitten was lost.
It was lost in the grass.
The kitten was sad.
A little girl saw the kitten.
She took the kitten home.

1. What was lost?

_____

2. Where was it lost?

_____

3. What colour was the kitten?

_____

4. Who saw the kitten?

_____

5. How did the kitten feel?

_____

6. What did the girl do with the kitten?

_____

Pam's Birthday

Name _____

It is Pam's birthday.
All her friends will come.
They will get hooters and hats.
They will eat cake and ice cream.
Pam and her friends will have fun
at her party.

1. Who is having a birthday?

_____

2. Who will come to the party?

_____

3. What will her friends get?

_____

4. What will they eat?

_____

5. Who will have fun?

_____

6. Where will they have fun?

_____

The Turtle and the Beetle

Name _____

It was a bright afternoon.

A little turtle swam in the pond.

It swam very slowly.

The turtle saw a black beetle.

The black beetle jumped away.

1. What was the afternoon like?

   _____

2. Is the turtle big or little?

   _____

3. Where did the turtle swim?

   _____

4. How did the turtle swim?

   _____

5. What did the turtle see?

   _____

6. What did the beetle do?

   _____

Ben's Frog

Name _____

Ben had a frog in a box.
The frog was little and green.
Ben found it in the park.
The frog was by a rock.
He gave it to his friend.

1. What did Ben have?

_____

2. Where did Ben keep his frog?

_____

3. What colour was the frog?

_____

4. Where did Ben find the frog?

_____

5. What was by the rock?

_____

6. What did Ben do with the frog?

_____

The Frog

Name _____

The little frog sat in the pond.

The frog sat very still.

A little fly flew by.

The frog jumped up and ate the fly.

Then the frog swam away.

1. Where did the frog sit?

_____

2. Was the frog big or little?

_____

3. How did the frog sit?

_____

4. What flew by?

_____

5. What did the frog do when it saw the fly?

_____

6. What did the frog do then?

_____

Jan and the Beetle

Name _____

Jan saw something on a flower.
It was a little, red beetle.
The beetle did not fly away.
It walked on Jan's hand.
Jan was happy with her new pet.

1. What did Jan see?

   _____

2. Where did Jan see the beetle?

   _____

3. What colour was the beetle?

   _____

4. Did the beetle fly away?

   _____

5. Where did the beetle walk?

   _____

6. Was Jan happy with her new pet?

   _____

Comprehension, KS1

The Squirrel

Skill: Literal
comprehension

Name _____

The little grey squirrel ran.
It saw a bag in the grass.
The squirrel looked into the bag.
It found a little peanut.
The squirrel ate the peanut.

1. What ran?

_____

2. What did the squirrel look like?

_____

3. What was in the grass?

_____

4. Where did the squirrel look?

_____

5. What did the squirrel find?

_____

6. What did the squirrel do with the peanut?

_____

Comprehension, KS1

The Lost Aeroplane

Name _____

Ted ran up the hill.
He ran after a toy aeroplane.
The aeroplane flew into a tree.
Ted could not get the plane down.
He will have to get help.

1. Where did Ted run?

_____

2. What did Ted run after?

_____

3. What kind of aeroplane was it?

_____

4. Where did the plane go?

_____

5. Did Ted get the plane?

_____

6. What will Ted do?

_____

Comprehension, KS1

The Mouse

Name _____

The little brown mouse walked very softly.

The mouse sniffed.

It could smell something good.

It saw a little cookie.

The mouse ate the cookie.

1. How did the mouse walk?

   _____

2. What sniffed?

   _____

3. What colour was the mouse?

   _____

4. What did the mouse smell?

   _____

5. What did the mouse see?

   _____

6. What did the mouse do?

   _____

The Clown

Name _____

Come and see Pat's father in the circus.
Pat's dad is a funny clown.
Sometimes he drives a car.
Sometimes a seal rides with him.
Children laugh and clap.

1. Who will you come to see?

   _____

2. Where will you see Pat's father?

   _____

3. What is Pat's father?

   _____

4. What does he drive?

   _____

5. What rides with Pat's father sometimes?

   _____

6. What do the children do?

   _____

Tom's Box

Name _____

Tom got a big, brown box.
He got it from his father.
Tom wants to make a clubhouse.
Tom will paint it.
His friends will like it.

1. What did Tom get?

_____

2. What did the box look like?

_____

3. Where did he get the box?

_____

4. What did Tom want to make?

_____

5. What will Tom do with the box?

_____

6. Who will like the clubhouse?

_____

Comprehension, KS1

Linda's Mask

Name _____

Linda went to the toyshop.
She wanted to get a funny mask.
She got a mask with a big, red nose.
She wanted to surprise Mum
and Dad.
Mum and Dad laughed.

1. Where did Linda go?

_____

2. What did she want to get?

_____

3. What mask did Linda get?

_____

4. What kind of nose did the mask have?

_____

5. Who did Linda want to surprise?

_____

6. What did Mum and Dad do?

_____

Rain

Skill: Literal comprehension

Name _____

Mike was playing ball in the garden.
Something wet fell on his head.
Mike looked up and saw dark clouds.
It began to rain and Mike got wet.
He ran into the house.

1. Where was Mike?

_____

2. What was Mike doing?

_____

3. What fell on his head?

_____

4. What did Mike see?

_____

5. Why did Mike get wet?

_____

6. Where did Mike go?

_____

Comprehension, KS1

The Owl and the Mouse

Name _____

Skill: Literal
comprehension

It was night.
A little grey mouse was running.
A big owl was after it.
The mouse hid in the grass.
The owl did not get the mouse.

1. Was it morning or night?

_____

2. What was running?

_____

3. What was after the mouse?

_____

4. Where did the mouse hide?

_____

5. What colour was the mouse?

_____

6. Did the owl get the mouse?

_____

Comprehension, KS1

Skill: Literal comprehension

Name _____

Frank goes to the library every Monday.

Frank likes to read books.

He likes books about dinosaurs.

Frank reads books to
his little brother.

His brother likes to hear Frank read.

1. Where does Frank go?

_____

2. When does he go to the library?

_____

3. What books does he like?

_____

4. To whom does Frank read?

_____

5. Is Frank's brother big or little?

_____

6. Does Frank's brother like to hear him read?

_____

A Brave Girl

Name _____

Kim is brave. She will pet a snake. She will climb a tree. She will eat liver. She does not cry in the dark. She will pull a loose tooth right out. Wow!

1. Who is brave?

_____

2. What will Kim climb?

_____

3. What will Kim eat?

_____

4. What will Kim pet?

_____

5. What will she do with a loose tooth?

_____

Comprehension, KS1

Bob's Job

Name _____

Bob helps his mum. He feeds the fish. He can brush his own teeth. He puts the rubbish out in the bin. He can take the baby out for a walk in the buggy. When it gets dark, he puts the dog out in the garden.

1. Who does Bob help?

_____

2. What does Bob brush?

_____

3. What does Bob feed?

_____

4. Who does Bob take for a walk?

_____

5. When does Bob put the dog out?

_____

6. What does Bob put in the bin?

_____

★7. How do **you** help at home? Draw a picture of what you do.

Play Ball!

Name _____

Tom had a big red ball. He hit the ball with his new blue bat. The ball hit a rose bush. Oh no! It popped. Then Sue came. She had a green ball. Now Tom and Sue can play ball.

1. Who had a green ball?

_____

2. Where is the red ball?

_____

3. What is new and blue?

_____

4. Why did the ball pop?

_____

★5. Draw a ball game **you** like!

Comprehension, KS1

Run, Rat, Run!

Name _____

Ben, the cat, ran after the rat. The rat hid in a box. The cat saw the rat. Then the rat ran out the door. Ben ran out too. When Ben came back, he was very fat. I think he got that rat!

1. Who is Ben?

    _____

2. Where did the rat hide first?

    _____

3. Then where did the rat run?

    _____

4. Who is fat now?

    _____

★ 5. Draw a big fat cat.

Comprehension, KS1

At The Zoo

Skill: Literal comprehension

Name _____

My aunty took me to the zoo. We saw a lion. It was asleep. We saw a big red and green bird. It said,"My name is Polly." I fed a baby goat. It ate an ice cream cone. I got a toy bear on the way out. It cost 80 pence.

1. Who took me to the zoo?

_____

2. What did the bird say?

_____

3. What was asleep?

_____

4. Who ate an ice cream cone?

_____

5. What did I buy?

_____

★6. Draw some zoo animals.

The Big Mess

Name _____

My room is a mess. I have a pet bird and a pet rat. They drop seeds everywhere. I stuff my toys under the bed. My coat is on the chair. My shoes are on the floor. My books are all over the desk. My cat leaves hair on the rug.

1. Where is the mess?

_____

2. Where are the toys?

_____

3. Where are the shoes?

_____

4. Where are the books?

_____

5. Who drops seeds?

_____

6. How does the cat make a mess?

_____

★ 7. Draw **your** room.

Comprehension, KS1

Name _____

Jim sat on a pin. It hurt, so he began to cry. Sue was sad to see Jim cry. She gave him a hug and a kiss. She gave him an apple too. That made Jim smile. He liked that apple. Munch, Munch!

1. Why did Jim cry?

   _____

2. Who saw Jim cry?

   _____

3. What did Sue give Jim? (3 things)

   _____

4. What did Jim like?

   _____

⭐ 5. Did **you** ever get hurt?
   Draw a picture of that time.

Comprehension, KS1

Would you Believe it?

Name _____

Fred had a new book. He read it to Bill and Pam. It was about a dog as big as a house. The dog was purple. It came to school. It gave the children a ride on its tail. When the teacher saw that dog in the playground, she jumped up in a tree.

1. Who had a new book?

_____

2. Who heard the story?

_____

3. What was the book about?

_____

4. What did the dog do for the children?

_____

5. What did the teacher do when she saw it?

_____

★ 6. Draw the dog.

Rover

Name _____

Bill likes dogs, but they make him sneeze. His mum gave him a turtle. Its name is Rover. It eats dog food and worms. Bill made a tiny house for it. Rover does not like cold days. When it is cold, Rover goes to sleep.

Here, Rover!

1. Who is Rover?

_____

2. Why can't Bill have a dog?

_____

3. What does Rover eat?

_____

4. What did Bill make?

_____

5. Who gave Rover to Bill?

_____

6. What does Rover do on cold days?

_____

Comprehension, KS1

More Rain, Please!

Name _____

I love rain. When there is a lot of rain, it makes a pond in our garden. Frogs lay eggs in the mud. After five weeks, you can find baby frogs in the water. Last year, I got nine frogs. I kept them in a bucket for a while.
Then I let them go.

1. Why do I like rain?

   _____

2. Where do the frogs lay the eggs?

   _____

3. How long do you wait to see the baby frogs?

   _____

4. How many did I get last year?

   _____

5. Where did I keep them?

   _____

plop

★ 6. Why do you think I let them go?

46

Gulp!

Name _____

Once I ate an insect. I did not mean to. Sally said. "Look up at that tree. See all the insects on it." I looked up. An insect fell right into my mouth. My mum was sick when I told her about it. She had to lie down.

1. What did I eat?

_____

2. How did it get in to my mouth?

_____

3. Who was with me?

_____

4. Who was sick?

_____

5. What did Mum have to do?

_____

Comprehension, KS1

T.V. Time

Name _____

Sam likes T.V. His dad lets Sam see one show each day. Last night Sam saw a show about a shark. It gave him a bad dream. Today Sam wants to see a show about dogs. Sam likes shows about animals best.

1. How much T.V. can Sam see each day?

   _____

2. What gave Sam a bad dream?

   _____

3. What show will Sam see today?

   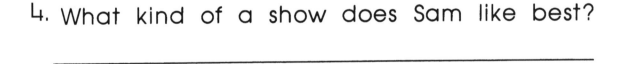

   _____

4. What kind of a show does Sam like best?

   _____

★5. What T.V. show do **you** like best?
   Make a picture of it.

48

Quack!

Name _____

The duck saw a bag of corn. She said, "I want to eat some corn." But the corn was up too high. She asked the pig to help. She climbed up on his head. She made a hole in the bag with a stick. Then the corn fell out.

1. Who saw the corn?

_____

2. Why was it hard to get?

_____

3. How did the pig help?

_____

4. How did they get the corn out of the bag?

_____

★5. Draw two more farm animals.

Comprehension, KS1

Is That True?

Name _____

I saw two little green men last Sunday. They came down in a grey ship. They came from the moon. My dog, Fred did not like them. He bit one. The moon man hit Fred with a paintbrush. That is how Fred got those black spots on his tail.

1. When did the moon men come?

   _____

2. What colour are they?

   _____

3. How did they get here?

   _____

4. Who did not like them?

   _____

5. How did Fred get his spots?

   _____

★6. Draw two green moon men.

Here We Go

Skill: Literal
comprehension

Name _____

I go on the bus to school. I sit by Sue. We sit at the back of the bus. We like to sing as we go. Once Tom sat with us. He read a book in his lap. The three of us are in Room 6. Miss Green is our teacher. She is so nice!

1. How do I get to school?

_____

2. Where do Sue and I sit?

_____

3. What do we do on the bus?

_____

4. What did Tom do on the bus?

_____

5. Who is our teacher?

_____

6. Do you think we like her?

_____

★7. Draw **your** teacher.

Bye, Bye!

Comprehension, KS1

At The Shop

Name _____

Mr. Green has a shop. Mum took our baby to the shop. His name is Timmy. He likes to ride in the trolley. Mum got some eggs. Timmy gave the eggs a toss. They fell on the floor. What a mess! Mr. Green used a mop. He was not cross. He said Timmy was a cute baby. That made Mum smile.

1. Who is Mr. Green?

   _____

2. Who is Timmy?

   _____

3. Where did Timmy ride?

   _____

4. How did Timmy make a mess?

   _____

5. What made Mum smile?

   _____

★ 6. Draw some things **you** can get at the shop?

Skill: Literal comprehension

Name _____

My mum goes to night school on Monday. Dad and I make our own dinner. We are good cooks. Last week we made pizza, tomato soup, and gingerbread. Billy Green came to eat with us. His mum sent a fresh apple pie. Yum! We ate it all. Then we had to clean up our mess. Yuk!

1. Where is Mum on Monday night?

_____

2. What kind of soup did we have?

_____

3. What kind of pie did we have?

_____

4. Who came to dinner with Dad and me?

_____

5. Who sent the pie?

_____

6. What did we have to do last?

_____

Comprehension, KS1

The Big Box

Name _____

Uncle David had a big brown box for Kate. It had four little holes in the side. Kate took a peep. She saw some hay in the box. She saw some black fur too. Mum cut the string and took the top off the box. A big black rabbit hopped out! Then Kate saw some tiny pink things move in the hay.

1. What do you think the tiny pink things are?

   _____

2. How did Kate peek in the box?

   _____

3. What colour was the big rabbit?

   _____

4. What colour was the box?

   _____

5. How did Mum open the box?

   _____

6. How did the rabbit get air in the box?

   _____

7. What was in the box to make a soft nest?

   _____

My Sister

Name _____

Peg is my little sister. She will eat just three things: bananas, hot dogs, and milk. She has a doll named Pat. Pat has no hair. It all fell off when Peg put her in the bath. Peg does not like the dark, so she has a little night light by her bed. The light looks like a frog.

munch

1. Who is **Pat**?

   _____

2. What will Peg eat?

   _____

3. Why is Pat bald?

   _____

4. What looks like a frog?

   _____

★ 5. Draw someone in **your** family.

Lisa's New Pet

Name _____

Lisa found a little, brown puppy.

She took it home and gave it a bath.

She gave the puppy good food
to eat.

The puppy did not have a home.

Lisa will keep the puppy.

1. What did Lisa find?

_____

2. What colour was the puppy?

_____

3. Did the puppy have a home?

_____

4. Where did Lisa take the puppy?

_____

5. What is one thing Lisa did for the puppy?

_____

6. Do you think Lisa was good to the puppy?

_____

Comprehension, KS1

The Little Pig

Name _____

The Little Pig

Fred Green has a pet pig.
It is little and white with a curly tail.
The pig likes to roll in the mud.
When the pig gets muddy, Fred
Green gives it a bath.

1. Who has a pet pig?

   _____

2. What does the pig look like?

   _____

3. What kind of tail does it have?

   _____

4. What does the pig like to do?

   _____

5. When does Fred Green give his pig a bath?

   _____

6. Do you think the pig will like a bath?

   _____

Comprehension, KS1

The Bird

Name _____

Skill: Literal and inferential comprehension

My friend has a pet bird.

It is a pretty, green bird.

It likes to eat seeds.

It can talk and sing.

Sometimes it just makes a lot of noise.

1. What does my friend have?

_____

2. What does the bird look like?

_____

3. What does the bird eat?

_____

4. What can the bird do?

_____

5. Do you think the bird can dance?

_____

6. What does it do sometimes?

_____

Comprehension, KS1

Mother Alligators

Name _____

A mother alligator takes good care of her babies. First, she makes a nest out of grass and plants. Next, she lays her eggs in the nest. Later, she helps the babies come out of their eggs. She feeds them and lets them ride on her head!

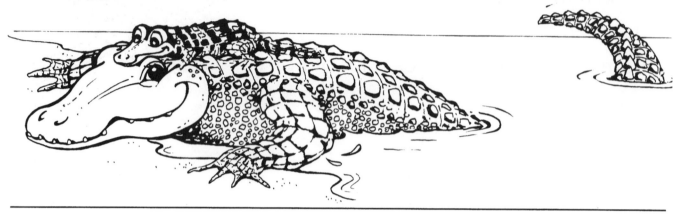

Circle the best answer.

1. What animal is this story about?

   armadillo   **alligator**

2. What kind of mother is an alligator?

   good   **bad**

3. Which sentence tells about the whole story?
   Draw a green line under that sentence.

Try This!

- Baby alligators eat small fish. Draw two fish in the picture above.
- Find out what colour alligators are. Colour the picture to match.

Camping Out

Name _____

On a camping trip, it is important to have certain things. First, you need a tent. You also need some food and an ice box. Pack your sleeping bags and some kind of light, too. Don't forget your pillows and some rain gear!

---

1. What kind of trip is this story about?

    long   **camping**   **class**

2. Reread the story. Draw a line under the sentence that tells about the whole story.

Try This!

- Pretend you are going on a camping trip. Make a list of the things you would take with you.
- Draw a picture of you and your family on a camping trip.

Name _____

Breakfast is important! It helps your body all day. There are many tasty things to eat for breakfast. Have you ever eaten muffins, strawberries, and milk? Eggs, toast, and orange also make a good breakfast. Ask your mum about other healthy foods to eat in the morning.

Draw a line to make a correct sentence.

1. This story is about   morning.

2. We eat breakfast in the   breakfast.

3. Breakfast is   important.

4. Eating breakfast   helps your body.

Try This!

- Draw a picture of your favourite breakfast.
- Think up a new, healthy breakfast. Try it out.

Name _____

If you get a puppy, you must take care of it. It will need food and water. You will have to give your puppy baths. If your puppy has long fur, you will need to brush it. Don't forget to clean up after the puppy!

1. What is this story mostly about?

   baths   **a playful puppy**   **taking care of a puppy**

2. Draw a line under the sentence that tells about the whole story.

   A puppy is fun.

   You must work hard to take care of a puppy.

   You should go and get a puppy.

3. Write the name of what this story tells about.

   _____

Try This!

- Write a story about a different kind of baby animal.
- Decide whether or not your baby animal would be a good pet.

Comprehension, KS1

Buttons

Name _____

Buttons help hold our clothes together. They are also fun to look at. They come in many shapes and colours. Most buttons are shaped like circles. Some look like pumpkins, pencils, or pigs. What would we do without buttons?

Circle the best answer.

1. How many button shapes did the story tell about?

    two   five   three   four

2. Which shape was in this story?

    apple   triangle   circle

3. Which button in this story is probably pink?

Try This!

• Draw a picture of a button you would like. What kinds of clothes would you put it on?

• Count the kinds of buttons you have on your clothes. How many different kinds are there?

The Striped Skunk

Name _____

A striped skunk is a small, black animal. Two white stripes run down its back. During the day, a striped skunk sleeps in a hole. It wakes up at night to look for food. A skunk can make a terrible smell when it is scared.

Circle the best answer.

1. What kind of skunk is this story about?

   hog-nosed   **striped**   **spotted**

2. The striped skunk sleeps

   in a hole.

   in a tree.

   inside a cave.

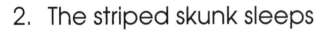

3. What does the skunk do when it is scared?

   _____

Try This! Learn about another kind of skunk. What do you think would happen if the two different kinds of skunks met each other?

64

The Ostrich

Name _____

An ostrich is a huge bird. It is the biggest bird in the world. The ostrich is so big, it cannot fly! It can run fast, though.

It can run faster than most of its enemies. Who do you think can run faster, you or an ostrich?

1. What is the biggest bird in the world? _____

2. Why can't an ostrich fly? _____

   _____

3. How can an ostrich get away from its enemies?

   _____

• Find out what colour an ostrich is. Colour the picture at the top of the page.

Comprehension, KS1

Name _____

Sometimes a sunny day can turn into a rainy day. First, grey clouds cover the sun. Soon, more clouds come. These clouds make the sky look grey, too. Soon, drops of water fall from the clouds. Everything on the ground gets wet.

1. Draw a line under the thing that happens first in the story.

    Raindrops fall from the clouds.

    Clouds cover the sun.

    More and more clouds come.

2. Write what happens last in the story on this line.

    _____

Try This!

- Draw a picture of a different kind of weather.
- Write one sentence to tell about the weather you chose.

Butterfly Babies

Name _____

Do you know where butterflies come from? First, a mother butterfly lays her eggs. About a week later, caterpillars come out of the eggs. They eat plants for about a month. Then they stick themselves to leaves and go to sleep. As they sleep, they lose their caterpillar skins and change into butterflies!

1. Write **1** in front of the thing that happens first.
   Write **2** in front of what happens second.
   Write **3** in front of what happens third.

   _____ **The caterpillars go to sleep.**

   _____ **The mother butterfly lays eggs.**

   _____ **They hatch.**

2. Circle the thing that happens last in the story.

   They eat plants.

   They become butterflies.

- Read a book to find out how butterflies eat. What do they do first? second? third?
- How do you eat? List the steps.

Comprehension, KS1

A Country Visit

Name _____

Have you ever been to the country? The air smells clean and fresh. You can see many trees and flowers. There are not many buildings. You may see a farm where horses and cows live. Or you might see a farm where fruit grows!

1. Use a brown crayon to circle any animal words.

2. Use a green crayon to underline any plant words.

3. Draw a yellow line through the sentence that tells about the flowers.

Try This! Draw a farm. Draw one cow and one horse. Make the sky blue. Draw two clouds and a sun.

Comprehension, KS1

Ladybird Tricks

Name _____

What can a ladybird do when it is in danger? It can play dead. The ladybird rolls on its back and stays still. Or, it can put out a liquid that tastes and smells rotten. Animals will not eat a dead or bad-tasting insect! These tricks work!

1. Colour the ladybird in the picture red. Make its spots black.

2. Colour the bird blue

3. Draw a leaf under the ladybird. Colour the leaf green.

Try This!

- Go on a ladybird hunt. How many did you find?
- Look for ladybirds that are not red. What other colours did you see?

Comprehension, KS1

Pumpkin Fun

Name _____

What fun things can you do with a pumpkin? You can eat its seeds! First, take them out of the pumpkin. Wash them. Then bake them. Put salt on the baked seeds and eat them. After you clean out the pumpkin shell, carve a funny face on it. This makes a jack-o'-lantern!

1. Use a pencil to draw a line under the longest word that you see in this story. Write the word. _____ How many times did you underline the word? _____

2. What is inside a pumpkin? _____ Draw an X on that word each time you see it in the story.

3. Draw an orange circle around the sentence that is a question.

Try This!

- Write all the steps, in order, that you have to follow to make a jack-o'-lantern.
- Draw pictures to show the most important steps.

Comprehension, KS1

Crows and Scarecrows

Name _____

Crows are big black birds. They eat seeds and plants because they like them. That makes farmers angry! So the farmers make scarecrows out of straw and old clothes. Scarecrows look like farmers. This scares crows and helps save plants!

1. Why do crows eat seeds and plants? _____

    _____

2. What happens when crows eat plants? _____

    _____

3. What happens when a farmer puts a scarecrow in a field? _____

Try This!

- Draw a picture of a scarecrow that would really scare away crows.
- Find out what else crows eat besides plants and seeds.

Let's Play Soccer

Name _____

In soccer, you must be careful how you touch the ball. There is a kickoff to start the game. After that, only one player can touch the ball using hands. Most players can touch the ball only with other body parts. If a player on one team uses hands, the other team gets the ball. Some players use their heads to try to hit the ball into the net for a point!

_____

1. What makes soccer such a hard game to learn to play?

   _____

2. What happens if a player on one team touches the ball with hands? _____

   _____

3. Why do some players use their heads to hit the ball?

   _____

 Draw a picture of a different kind of sport.

72

A Riddle

Name _____

People make up riddles to have fun with words. It's hard to answer riddles. If you answer one, it makes you laugh. This is an old riddle: "What has eyes but can't see?" If you think about it, you can answer it. The answer is *a potato*. Are you surprised? If you ask your friends this riddle, you can surprise them, too.

Circle the best answer.

1. If you think about it, what can you do with a riddle?

   Answer it.   **Throw it away.**   **Forget it.**

2. If you ask your friends this riddle, what can you do?

   Help them.   **Surprise them.**   **Feed them.**

3. Why do people make up riddles?

   to have fun with words   **to stay awake**

Try This!

- Read a book of riddles. How many did you guess?
- Make up a riddle. Tell it to a friend.

Comprehension, KS1

Grey Squirrels and Red Squirrels

Name _____

These two squirrels are alike in some ways. They are also different in some ways. A grey squirrel is bigger than a red squirrel. They both live in the forest. Many grey squirrels are slow. Red squirrels are the noisiest and busiest squirrels. In most years, both red and grey squirrels have two lots of babies.

_____

1. Which kind of squirrel is bigger? _____

2. Both red and grey squirrels

   live in forests.   **eat nuts.**   **are big.**

3. What other thing is different for red squirrels and grey squirrels? _____

4. What other thing is the same for both squirrels?

   _____

Try This!   Learn about one other kind of squirrel. How is it the same as red and grey squirrels? How is it different?

Baseball or Basketball?

Name _____

Baseball and basketball are games. Both are played with a ball. Nine children play in a baseball team. They play outside with a small, white ball and a bat. Five children play in a basketball team. They use a large, brown ball and a net. Basketball can be played inside or outside.

1. What is the name of a game played with a small, white ball? _____

2. Which game is played with five people in a team?

   _____

3. Name the game that children can play inside or outside.

   _____

4. Which game has nine children in a team?

   _____

Try This!

- Learn to play a new game that uses a ball.
- Find out more about baseball or basketball. Explain to a friend how to play the game.

75

Dr. Seuss

Name _____

Many years ago, a man named Theodor Geisel began writing books for children. They were silly books with many funny pictures and words. He called himself Dr. Seuss. Dr. Seuss wanted beginning readers to have a funny book to read. So he wrote *The Cat in the Hat*. Children loved the book, and they still do. Do you?

_____

Circle the best answer.

1. Dr. Seuss was probably

   funny.   **sad.**   **unfriendly.**

2. Which sentence about Dr. Seuss is most true?

   He was not fond of children.

   He didn't like to do nice things for people.

   He was a kind man.

3. How do you think Dr. Seuss would feel if he knew how much children like his books? _____

Try This! Learn all about a different person who writes children's books. Read some books by that person. What kind of person would write those books?

Brave Bessie

Name _____

Bessie Coleman was the first black woman to fly a plane. Many people told her she couldn't do it. She kept trying. Soon she could do hard tricks. She liked doing them at air shows. People came from all over the world to see brave Bessie fly.

Circle the best answer.

1. From the story, we know that Bessie

    always did what other people said to do.

    did what she believed she could do.

2. From the story, you can tell that Bessie

    didn't do hard things.   **tried to do hard things.**

3. Bessie did hard tricks, so we know she was

    brave.   **afraid.**   **shy.**

4. Think of one word to describe Bessie. _____

Try This!

- List three reasons you would like to have known Bessie.
- Write five sentences about the hardest thing you have learned to do.

Comprehension, KS1

Queen Elizabeth I

Name _____

Skill: Character analysis

Elizabeth I was born in 1533. That was more than 466 years ago! When she was 25 years old, she became Queen of England. While she was queen, the country became great. Her life was never easy, though. Before she was queen, she was put in prison. Most of her people thought she was a good queen. Elizabeth ruled England for 45 years. She died at the age of 70.

Circle the best answer.

1. What kind of queen do you think Elizabeth I was?

    good   **sweet**   **lucky**

2. From the story, we can tell that Elizabeth

    was probably a lazy person.

    would probably be easy to scare.

    was probably a hard worker.

Try This!

Would you like to be a queen or king? Why or why not?

Comprehension, KS1

Ocean Waves

Name _____

The ocean is not flat and smooth. It has waves that move and splash. Wind pushes on ocean water and makes waves. A little wind makes small waves. A strong wind makes big waves. What might happen during a storm?

Circle the best answer.

1. On a day with only a little wind, there will be

   big waves.   **small waves.**

2. If a big storm comes, there will probably be

   a strong wind.   **no wind.**

3. A strong wind on the ocean makes

   big waves.   **little waves.**

Try This!

- Draw a picture of a day at the beach with just a little wind.
- Draw another picture to show what the ocean would look like when a strong wind is blowing.

Comprehension, KS1

Where Does Water Go?

Name _____

Have you ever left water outside in a cup for a few days? Had the water gone when you went back to get it? The heat from the sun turned the water into tiny drops. These drops went up into the air and made a cloud. After many more tiny drops of water went into the cloud, it got heavy and grey.

1. The sun's heat makes the little drops of water

   melt.   **go up into the air.**   **turn into ice.**

2. What will happen after the cloud gets heavy and grey?

   _____

   _____

3. What do you think happens to the rainwater in puddles?

   _____

   _____

Put a little water in a cup outside. Mark the cup to show how much water you put in it. Check the water every day. How much is left after a week? Where do you think it went?

Comprehension, KS1

Popcorn

Name _____

Americans made popcorn first. They dried corn in the sun. Then they popped it in a fire. Popcorn must get hot to pop. Today we pop it in cooking oil. When the oil gets hot, the corn cooks. Soon, it pops into fluffy pieces. Then we let it cool. Popcorn makes a tasty treat.

1. What do you think happened after the Americans popped their corn? _____

2. If you don't heat popcorn, what will happen?

   _____

3. Put a bowl of popcorn in a room full of children. What will probably happen? _____

4. If you try to eat hot popcorn, what might happen?

   _____

Try This!

- Make a list of your friends and people in your family. Guess if they like popcorn. Circle those names in red.
- Find out how many of your friends like popcorn. How many times did you guess correctly?

Comprehension, KS1

Whale Watch

Name _____

The blue whale is the largest mammal ever. Its skin looks a little bit blue and spotty. It has a wide mouth. It eats tiny shrimps.

The grey whale is smaller than the blue whale. A grey whale also eats small shrimps Its mouth is smaller than a blue whale's mouth. The skin of a grey whale is dark grey with some white marks.

1. If you see a whale eating tiny shrimps, it must be a blue whale.　　**true**　　　　**false**

2. There are two whales swimming near your boat. One is huge and has a very wide mouth. It also has blue, spotty skin. It is probably a _____.

3. After reading this story, do you think a whale would make a good pet? _____ Why or why not? _____

_____

Draw a picture of these two whales the way you think they look. Then find pictures of the way they really look. Were you right?

Comprehension, KS1

Hamsters

Name _____

A hamster is a small, furry animal. It looks like a mouse. But a hamster has a short tail. Hamsters like to eat fruit, seeds, and plants. These chubby animals eat and play at night. Hamsters are fun to watch after the sun sets.

Circle the best answer.

1. If my pet looks like a mouse but has a long tail,

   it is probably a hamster.

   it is not a hamster.

2. In the daytime, a hamster probably

   sleeps.

   eats and plays.

3. From the story, we can tell that a hamster

   is not skinny.

   is fat.

   probably has a long tail.

Read a book about a hamster. Write your own story about this animal. Where does it live? What does it eat?

Comprehension, KS1

A Summer Garden

Name _____

Summer gardens are full of life. Plants grow in the warm sun. Many kinds of animals live there. Some animals are bees, butterflies, and worms. Gardeners like these animals. They help keep plants healthy. Some animals hurt gardens, though. Caterpillars and snails eat plant leaves! Gardeners do not like caterpillars or snails.

1. After reading the story, write what happens to plants in the summer. _____

_____

2. We can tell from the story that a gardener likes bees, butterflies, and worms because

   they eat plants.

   they are good for a garden.

3. Why are bees, butterflies, and worms good for a garden? _____

Try This! Choose one of the insects that a gardener likes. Find out how it is good for a garden.

A Peach

Name _____

A peach is a round fruit that grows on a tree. In spring, a flower grows on a peach tree. Next, a small, green peach begins to grow where the flower was. This green peach is hard, like a rock. As the air gets warmer, the peach grows bigger. It turns a pinkish-orange colour and ripens. Then it's time to pick and eat this juicy fruit!

Circle the best answer.

1. We don't eat green peaches because

    they are not ripe.

    we like the colour pink better.

2. A round red fruit is probably not

    a peach.

    an apple.

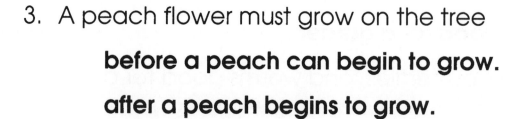

3. A peach flower must grow on the tree

    before a peach can begin to grow.

    after a peach begins to grow.

Try This!

- Write a sentence to end this story.
- Draw a picture to show what happened at the end of the story.

Comprehension, KS1

Which Water

Skill: Alike and different

Name _____

You can find water in a bay and a lake. You can ride a boat in a bay and on a lake. The water in a bay leads out to an ocean or a sea. Sometimes it leads to a large lake. The water in a lake has land all around it. Both bays and lakes can have beaches. Most bays are made of salt water. Most lakes have fresh water in them.

1. Circle the sentence that tells how a lake and a bay are different.

   A bay is bigger than a lake.

   A lake has water all around it.

   A lake has land all around it.

2. A lake and a bay can both have beaches

   true   **false**

3. Say one way in which lakes and bays are different.

4. A lake and a bay are each a kind of

   land.   **water.**   **animal.**

Now learn about two different kinds of land. How are they alike and how are they different?

Comprehension, KS1

A Peacock and a Parrot

Name _____

Parrots and peacocks are birds. A parrot is big, but a peacock is bigger! Both birds are colourful. Peacocks are mostly blue and green. Parrots can be green, red, white, purple, or blue! Both birds make noise, but some parrots talk. Peacocks never talk. Next time you go to a zoo, look for these birds.

Put an X in each box to tell how peacocks and parrots are alike or different.

	Alike	Different
1. The kind of animal		
2. Its colours		
3. Talking		
4. Noise		
5. Look for in zoo		

Try This!

- Find out what a peacock looks like. Draw a picture. Show its colours.
- Read a book on parrots. Which is your favourite? Draw its picture next to the peacock.
- Show a friend how these birds are alike and different.

Comprehension, KS1

Flats and Houses

Name _____

People live in flats. They also live in houses. There are rooms in flats and houses. Flats have doors. Houses have doors, too. Many families can live in a block of flats. Often only one family lives in a house. Where do you live?

1. In the story, draw a red circle around all the ways flats and houses are alike.

2. List two ways houses and flats are alike.

   _____

   _____

3. In the story, draw a green line under each way flats and houses are different.

4. List one way flats and houses are different.

   _____

Try This!

- Think of two ways flats and houses are different.
- Give this story a new title.

88

Answers

Page 1
Coloured yellow - bike, ball, doll, kite
Coloured red - hat, shoe, dress, coat
Coloured blue - cat, dog, hen, fish, pig

Page 2
1. red, blue, green, yellow
2. milk, egg, meat, apple
3. girl, mother, father, boy
4. five, one, three, four
5. ear, arm, hand, head, nose
6. rain, cloud, fog, snow
7. book, desk, pencil, flag
8. lamp, bed, door, sink, rug

Page 3
1. farm
2. dishes
3. tools
4. space
5. insects
6. food

Page 4
Answers will vary.

Page 5
1. plum
2. jump
3. four
4. shoes
5. blue
6. toes
7. month
8. dinner
9. butter
10. stars

Page 6
mother
pots
grass
soil
boy
flowers
gloves
plants
planting time

Page 7
Rabbit has a rest
Asleep for the Winter

Page 8
1. I Can Draw
2. On Her Toes
3. The New Dad
4. Run and Kick

Page 9
Answers will vary.

Page 10
Answers will vary.

Page 11
1. No   2. Yes
The dogs are big and little.
1. Yes 2. No
The chick is hatching.
1. No   2. Yes 3. No
She loves her pet.

Page 12
1. He did a magic trick.
2. She rides on the horse.
3. The funny clown juggles.
4. The dogs are silly.

Page 13
1. The cat hunts mice.
2. The bat can hang upside down.
3. The tree frog can climb.
4. The river otter is playing.
5. The giraffe is taller than the boy.

Page 14
1. The boy smells the flowers.
2. The bird feeds her babies.
3. It is a windy day.
4. The girl sees the butterfly.
5. The girl waters the flowers.

Page 15
Answers will vary.

Page 16
1. no
2. no
3. yes
4. no
They liked camping.

Page 17
1. no
2. no
3. no
4. yes
5. no
We went out for dinner.

Page 18
Nancy went on a hiking trip.
Space camp was great!

Page 19
Jean found her lost bear.
Jim got new shoes.
The cat wanted milk, too.

Page 20
Answers will vary but should be similar
to the following:
● Shelby can do tricks.
● Red Fox drove too fast.

Page 21
1. in the park
2. ran after a beetle
3. little
4. in the grass
5. Jack
6. no

Page 22
1. a kitten
2. in the grass
3. grey
4. a little girl
5. sad
6. took the kitten home

Page 23
1. Pam
2. all her friends
3. hooters and hats
4. cake and ice cream
5. at Pam's party

Page 24
1. bright
2. little
3. in the pond
4. slowly
5. a black beetle
6. jumped away

Page 25
1. a frog
2. in a box
3. green
4. in the park
5. the frog
6. gave it to his friend

Page 26
1. in the pond
2. little
3. very still
4. a little fly
5. jumped up and ate the fly
6. swam away

Page 27
1. something on a flower (beetle)
2. on a flower
3. red
4. no
5. on Jan's hand
6. yes

Page 28
1. a little, grey squirrel
2. little and grey
3. a bag
4. into the bag
5. a little peanut
6. ate the peanut

Page 29
1. up the hill
2. a toy aeroplane
3. toy
4. into a tree
5. no
6. get help

Page 30
1. very softly
2. the mouse
3. brown
4. something good (cookie)
5. a little cookie
6. ate the cookie

Comprehension, KS1

Answers

Page 31
1. Pat's father
2. in the circus
3. He is a clown
4. a car
5. a seal
6. laugh and clap

Page 32
1. a box
2. big and brown
3. from his father
4. a clubhouse
5. paint it
6. his friends

Page 33
1. to the toy shop
2. a funny mask
3. a mask with a big, red nose;
   a funny mask
4. big and red
5. Mum and Dad
6. laughed

Page 34
1. in the garden
2. playing ball
3. something wet (rain)
4. dark clouds
5. It began to rain.
6. into the house

Page 35
1. night
2. a mouse
3. a big owl
4. in the grass
5. grey
6. no

Page 36
1. to the library
2. every Monday
3. books about dinosaurs
4. his little brother
5. little
6. yes

Page 37
1. Kim
2. a tree
3. liver
4. a snake
5. She will pull it out.

Page 38
1. his mum
2. his teeth
3. the fish
4. the baby
5. when it is dark
6. the rubbish

Page 39
1. Sue
2. It popped.
3. Tom's bat
4. It hit the rose bush.

Page 40
1. the cat
2. in a box
3. out the door
4. Ben

Page 41
1. my aunt
2. My name is Polly.
3. the lion
4. the baby goat
5. a toy bear

Page 42
1. my room
2. under the bed
3. on the floor
4. all over the desk
5. the rat and the bird
6. It leaves hair on the rug.

Page 43
1. He sat on a pin.
2. Sue
3. a hug, a kiss and an apple
4. the apple

Page 44
1. Fred
2. Bill and Pam
3. a big purple dog
4. It gave them a ride.
5. She jumped up in a tree.

Page 45
1. the turtle
2. They make him sneeze.
3. dog food and worms
4. a tiny house for Rover
5. his mum
6. Rover goes to sleep.

Page 46
1. It makes a pond.
2. in the mud
3. five weeks
4. nine
5. in a bucket

Page 47
1. an insect
2. It fell out of a tree.
3. Sally
4. my mum
5. She had to lie down.

Page 48
1. one show
2. a show about a shark
3. a show about dogs
4. shows about animals

Page 49
1. the duck
2. It was up high.
3. The duck stood on his head.
4. The duck poked a hole with a stick.

Page 50
1. Sunday
2. green
3. in a grey ship
4. Fred, the dog
5. when the moon man hit him

Page 51
1. on the bus
2. at the back of the bus
3. We sing.
4. He read.
5. Miss Green
6. yes

Page 52
1. the shop owner
2. our baby
3. in the trolley
4. He tossed the eggs.
5. Mr. Green said Timmy was cute.

Page 53
1. at school
2. tomato soup
3. apple pie
4. Billy Green
5. Billy's mum
6. clean up

Page 54
1. baby rabbits
2. through a hole
3. black
4. brown
5. She cut the string
6. through the holes
7. hay

Page 55
1. Peg's doll
2. bananas, hot dogs and milk
3. Peg put her in the bath
4. the night light

Page 56
1. a puppy
2. brown
3. no
4. to her home
5. gave it a bath; gave it food
6. yes

Page 57
1. Fred Green
2. little and white
3. curly
4. roll in the mud
5. when it gets muddy
6. Answers will vary

Page 58
1. a pet bird
2. pretty and green
3. seeds
4. talk and sing
5. Answers will vary
6. makes a lot of noise

Comprehension, KS1

Answers

Page 59
1. an alligator
2. good
3. A mother alligator takes good care of her babies

Page 60
1. camping
2. On a camping trip, it is important to have certain things.

Page 61
1. This story is about breakfast.
2. We eat breakfast in the morning.
3. Breakfast is important.
4. Eating breakfast helps your body.

Page 62
1. taking care of a puppy
2. You must work hard to take care of a puppy.
3. puppies

Page 63
1. four 2. circle 3. pig

Page 64
1. striped
2. in a hole
3. It can make a terrible smell.

Page 65
1. the ostrich
2. It's too big to fly.
3. It can run fast.

Page 66
1. Clouds cover the sun.
2. Everything on the ground gets wet.

Page 67
1. (1) The mother butterfly lays eggs.
   (2) They hatch.
   (3) The caterpillars go to sleep.
2. They become butterflies.

Page 68
1. horses, cows
2. trees, flowers, fruit
3. You can see many trees and flowers.

Page 69
1. The ladybird should be coloured red with black spots.
2. The bird should be coloured blue.
3. A leaf should be drawn under the ladybird and coloured green.

Page 70
1. pumpkin; 3
2. seeds
3. What fun things can you do with a pumpkin?

Page 71
1. Crows eat plants and seeds because they like them.
2. When crows eat plants, the farmers get angry.
3. The scarecrow scares the crows and helps save plants.

Page 72
1. Only one person can touch the ball with hands.
2. The other team gets the ball.
3. To try to hit the ball into the net for a point.

Page 73
1. Answer it.
2. Surprise them.
3. to have fun with words

Page 74
1. grey squirrel
2. live in forests
3. Many grey squirrels are slow; red squirrels are very noisy and busy.
4. Both may have two lots of babies a year.

Page 75
1. baseball
2. basketball
3. basketball
4. baseball

Page 76
1. funny
2. He was a kind man.
3. Answers may vary

Page 77
1. did what she believed she could do
2. tried to do hard things
3. brave
4. Answers will vary

Page 78
1. good
2. was probably a hard worker

Page 79
1. small waves
2. a strong wind
3. big waves

Page 80
1. go up into the air
2. Rain will fall.
3. It turns into little drops of water and goes up in the air to form clouds.

Page 81
1. They ate it.
2. It will not pop.
3. They will eat it.
4. It might burn our mouths.

Page 82
1. false
2. blue whale
3. Answers will vary but most will say no. Answers will vary.

Page 83
1. it is not a hamster
2. sleeps
3. is fat

Page 84
1. Plants grow in the warm sun.
2. they are good for a garden
3. They help keep plants healthy.

Page 85
1. they are not ripe
2. a peach
3. before a peach can begin to grow

Page 86
1. A lake has land all around it
2. true
3. The water in a bay leads out to an ocean or a sea; most bays are made of salt water; most lakes have fresh water in them.
4. water

Page 87
1. Alike
2. Different
3. Different
4. Alike
5. Alike

Page 88
1. People live in flats. They also live in houses. There are rooms in flats and houses. Flats have doors. Houses have doors too.
2. Any two of the above answers can be written on the lines.
3. Many families can live in a block of flats. Often only one family lives in a house.
4. Any of the above or an answer the child comes up with.

Comprehension, KS1